INF FIC WIL

DO
NOT
WITHDRAW
FROM
STOCK

D1634915

Caerleon
Library

A MACDONALD BOOK

Text copyright © 1972 Barbara Willard
First published in Great Britain in 1972
by Hamish Hamilton Children's Books Ltd

Illustrations © 1988 George Buchanan

This edition published in Great Britain in 1988
by Macdonald & Co (Publishers) Ltd
London & Sydney
A member of Maxwell Pergamon Publishing Corporation plc

Photoset in 16pt Times by Keene Graphics Ltd, London
Colour origination by Scantrans Pte Ltd, Singapore

Printed and bound in Spain
by Cronion SA

Macdonald & Co (Publishers) Ltd
Greater London House
Hampstead Road
London NW1 7QX

BRITISH LIBRARY CATALOGUING IN PUBLICATION DATA
Willard, Barbara
The Dragon box.
I. Title II. Buchanan, George
823'.914[J]

ISBN 0-356-13948-4
ISBN 0-356-13949-2 Pbk

INF FIC WIL

Barbara Willard

T COLLEGE OF HIGHER EDUCATION LIBRARY

Illustrated by George Buchanan

Macdonald

Chapter One

Thomas's Uncle Ned was a tall broad man with a big bushy beard. His gold watch-chain glittered and looped across his large stomach. He was a little like some bold sea captain, for he had wandered the wide world since he was a lad. He lived and worked far away and sailed home to England only once in every three years.

Uncle Ned had no family of his own,
so he always stayed with his sister
Mary, and she was Thomas's mother.
When the letter came telling them that
Uncle Ned had been ill and was
returning for good to work in London,
there could be no doubt where he
would find a home.

"We shall look after him, and he will
look after us," said Thomas's mamma.
She was pleased and happy, as anyone
could see.

6

Thomas had been only a baby when his father died, and since then his mother must often have been lonely. It was very quiet with just her and Thomas, and old Florence who cooked and cleaned and cared for them both.

"Uncle Ned will take you to the Zoo," his mother told Thomas. "He will take me to the Opera. We shall all have a wonderful time."

It was already a year since Uncle Ned's last visit. A year to a boy of Thomas's age was a long time.

It was not only the hugeness and the roar of Uncle Ned that Thomas thought about as he sat at breakfast and watched his mother fold the letter back into its envelope. "Well; young Thomas," Uncle Ned had boomed as he said goodbye at the end of his last visit. "Here I go once more across the seas to the Land of the Dragon."

Ever since, Thomas had imagined Uncle Ned living with dragons prowling beyond his garden fence.

Could dragons be tamed, he wondered, to share the house like a dog? If so, Uncle Ned was surely the man to keep a dragon as a pet.

As soon as breakfast was over, Thomas went to the kitchen where Florence was clattering the dishes into the sink.

"Uncle Ned's coming to live," said Thomas.

"And a fine thing for all of us," cried Florence. "It'll be a pleasure to see a man about the house again."

"I don't want him," said Thomas.

"What's that? A fine man like him? And such a comfort for your poor dear mamma! That's no way to talk."

"But," said Thomas, kicking at the table leg and using a louder voice this time, "*I don't want him.* Why can't he stay with his old dragons?"

Florence looked at him over her spectacles that had been broken and mended with sticking plaster and cotton. "Dragons? What's dragons to do with it?"

"That's where Uncle Ned lives – in the Land of the Dragon. He told me. He'll be bringing one to live here with him."

"Your uncle lives in China, child."

"The Land of the Dragon. He said so."

"Maybe that's just a name for China. Don't they call Japan the Land of the Rising Sun? And aren't they next door to one another?"

"This dragon," insisted Thomas, as it grew faster than mustard-and-cress in his mind, faster than Jack's beanstalk, even, "this dragon will have very hot fiery breath. That's what all dragons have. It'll burn up the furniture."

11

"Now what are you talking about?" clucked Florence. "If you can't talk sense, away with you out of my kitchen."

"And your apron, too," Thomas persevered. "It'll burn up all our clothes. And the curtains. And the tablecloth, and it'll gnaw off the door handles so we won't be able to shut it out. It'll go huffing about the house – "

"That'll do!" cried Florence. "I'll give you dragons, you little fibbing monster!"

Chapter Two

Because Thomas had told Florence
about the dragon it seemed much
more real. He thought about it almost
all the time. Where would it live?
Would it come in a cage, like a parrot?
Where would it sleep? Would it curl up
by the kitchen fire, as their old dog
had done? Or in a basket of its own?
A box would be better – a very strong
box...

Soon Uncle Ned's dragon seemed so real to Thomas that he thought he knew exactly how it would feel to run his hand lightly down the creature's scaly back.

The spare bedroom now became known as Uncle Ned's room. Florence cleaned away every speck of dust while Mamma made new curtains. She snipped and stitched and whirred away at the sewing-machine.

"When will Uncle Ned come?" asked Thomas.

"He has a lot to do before he leaves. He will send on his luggage and then I can unpack for him."

Sure enough, one day the carrier's cart stopped at the door and unloaded two trunks, two huge boxes tied with cord, an enormous basket lashed with ropes, and a long package that looked like a huge drain-pipe sewn up in sacking.

"Oh I hope it is a beautiful Chinese carpet!" cried Mamma. "He always promised me one."

"Will there be a present for me?" asked Thomas.

"Of course. Uncle Ned would never forget a present for you, Thomas."

The boxes and packages were carried up to Uncle Ned's room. The keys had come separately, so Mamma unlocked the luggage and put Uncle Ned's clothes and belongings carefully away for him.

There were books in the two boxes, so a carpenter came and nailed some shelves to the wall, and the books were neatly arranged.

A picture of a sailing ship was hung up over the fireplace. A rocking chair with a cushion in a new cross-stitch cover was placed comfortably near the hearth.

Soon Thomas almost believed he could hear Uncle Ned moving about in his room already, coughing or blowing his nose, tapping out his pipe, singing to himself, snoring in the dark night time.

The year moved on and on. Thomas
had a birthday and then it was
Christmas. Everything was ready and
waiting for Uncle Ned, but he was
tossing somewhere on the ocean,
battered by storms, fighting against
wild and wintry gales.

Then one day the carrier came again. A huge box was carted in and set down in the hall. It was made of shiny black metal, very dented and scratched.

It was just possible to see that once the box had had a pattern painted all over it in gold paint. The paint was nearly worn away. Only here and there could be seen the outline of a flower, a spray of leaves, and the hint of a curly, swirling design.

"Why," cried Mamma, as the carrier set his load down in the narrow hall beneath the grandfather clock, "that's the Dragon Box!"

The Dragon Box was left lying in the hall. There was no key to open it, either among those that Uncle Ned had sent or anywhere in the house.

One after another they were tried and set aside.

"He doesn't want it unpacked," Thomas's mother decided.

"What might be in it?" Thomas asked warily, almost sure he knew.

"Perhaps it's full of wonderful presents," Mamma said. "He wants to hand them to us himself. We must wait till he gets here."

"There might be a dragon," Thomas said.

His mother laughed. "Oh I don't think so really."

"It is a Dragon Box," he reminded her.

"But that's because when it was new it had dragons painted all over it. It belonged to your grandpapa. It is very old."

"It's the right size for a dragon."

"Is it? Well, then – perhaps Uncle Ned has brought you a dragon for a present."

Thomas's heart leapt like a fish out of water. He saw at once that Uncle Ned was more likely to bring a dragon as a gift for his nephew than to bring his own – that might by now be rather big and old. For his nephew, Uncle Ned would have selected a young dragon, of a sensible size, better suited to a boy of Thomas's age.

After he had decided about this,
Thomas went nearly every day to the
box, and knelt down, and put his ear
against the side, listening intently for
any sound. There was none at all, but
he was certain that there in the dark
the creature lay sleeping. The fact that
it had no air and very little space
would make no difference to such a
magical beast.

Thomas could recall a story about a dragon shut up by a wizard in an airless cave for hundreds of years – but when the prince came and hacked his way in through the rock face, the dragon simply yawned and stretched and began at once to breath fire and flap his wings and lash his tail, just as he had done before his imprisonment.

Chapter Three

On a day in spring there was a sharp rat-tat on the door and there stood a telegraph boy.

"Telegram, ma'am."

"*Safe in port*," ran the message Mamma read out to Thomas. "*Arriving London Waterloo noon Thursday*."

Thomas's mother gave a shriek. "That's today! Florence! Florence, where are you? My dear brother is coming home this very day!"

She sounded so excited that Thomas thought she would cry. "He was so kind to me when I was a little girl," she said. "He was quite a big boy, but he took me everywhere with him."

"I'll go at once to the shops and buy a chicken to roast, ma'am," said Florence.

"Oh yes – and one of your best apple pies, Florence, and plenty of cream with it. And Stilton cheese. And port wine. It must be a feast of welcome!"

They went by cab to the station to meet Uncle Ned. Thomas wore his sailor suit and new boots, and Mamma her flowered bonnet. It was spring and the trees that stood along the river embankment were shaking into tender leaf.

At the station the sun slanted through the sooty glass roof and the noise of hissing steam, clattering wheels and shouting porters was almost frightening. As his mother hurried Thomas to the platform the train roared in and the passengers seemed to explode out of the doors.

Friends and relations began shouting
and waving, pushing and shoving.

"Can you see him, Mamma?"

"Not yet."

"Perhaps he's missed the train..."

"Then he'll catch the next one."

"The cab'll never wait. How shall we
get home...?"

"There! There he is! Look! Look,
Thomas! Here comes Uncle Ned at
last!"

Mamma rushed forward. As she met her brother she seemed almost to disappear in the great hug that he gave her.

Uncle Ned was not the absolute giant that Thomas had thought he remembered, but for an ordinary man he could not have been much bigger. And yet how kind and loving his smile was as he greeted his sister. And what warmth in his voice as he boomed out, "And where's young Thomas?"

If only there were just a little less of him, Thomas thought, it would be wonderful to see him.

There was so much to talk about, and it took so much time to show Uncle Ned his room, and his clothes tidy in the chest of drawers, and his suits hanging in the cupboard with his boots and shoes in a neat row beneath, that the welcome home feast was still going on at past five o'clock that evening.

Florence bustled round the table, urging Uncle Ned to another piece of chicken, another slice of ham, just a spoonful more potato. She cut generously into the apple pie, which must have been one of the best she had ever made, for its crust was like flakes of gold. She pressed the jug of cream into Uncle Ned's hands.

"You'll ruin me, Florence! Don't you know I've been ill once already, or I wouldn't be where I am today."

"You're over it," she assured him.
"I never saw you looking bonnier,
Mr Ned, and I've known you, man and
boy, for all of forty years." And she
wheedled him – "Another crumb of
this fine Stilton, sir? A drop more
port wine?"

"You'll build me up to twice my size,
Florence," he said, groaning. "Anyone
will tell you I'm quite big enough as it
is. What do you say, young Thomas?"

Thomas was sitting there chewing the last mouthful of his apple pie. Somehow he could not get rid of it, so he only nodded.

He had been quite unable to speak all this time, for he was torn in two by his feelings. Uncle Ned was so huge that he was also hugely kind – and that showed in his twinkling eyes and the way his big voice softened.

But Thomas was waiting for something, waiting all the time. He was waiting for Uncle Ned to speak of the Dragon Box, and how it must be unlocked, and what it contained...

It was not until Uncle Ned had drunk a second glass of port and lighted a little black cigar that the moment came.

"There's a fine carpet for you, Mary, in that great parcel of sacking," he told his sister. "Take my knife and get to opening it. Thomas and I have other things to see to. The Dragon Box has arrived safely, I observe."

The chewed apple pie settled itself in Thomas's left cheek.

"Is my present in there, Uncle Nèd?"

"For sure it is." Uncle Ned had pulled out the other end of his watch-chain and there dangled a key that looked as if it might be made of silver. He twiddled the key on the end of its chain, tilting back his chair a little, closing one eye against the smoke curling from his cigar.

"Shall we go and open the box, young Thomas?"

Thomas swallowed at last. "What's in it?"

"Now what would you expect to find in such a box?" Uncle Ned demanded.

"A dragon?" said poor Thomas, in a wobbly voice.

"That's certainly what I'd expect myself," agreed Uncle Ned. And he laughed enormously.

Thomas slid from his chair. He sidled out of the room and closed the door behind him. He was in the hall, with the Dragon Box on the floor at his side and the front door ahead of him. He ran to the front door and opened it, tugging because it was heavy, and then he was outside in the street. He ran.

Chapter Four

The spring day had died away into
dusk and the sky was misted. The
lamplighter was walking down the
street with his long pole over his
shoulder. One by one as he passed and
touched them with the pole, the lamps
came magically to life and shone
through the twilight like so many
golden moons.

Someone shouted, "Hi, Thomas!
Young Thomas, hi!"

Thomas ran on, with Uncle Ned
behind him striding easily.

Thomas got a terrible stitch in his
side, and he stopped, groaning.

Uncle Ned stopped, too. He did not
rush at Thomas and grab him, but
stood several paces away.

"What's up with you, you silly lad?"
he muttered, almost to himself.

Thomas shivered. His teeth
chattered. He could not speak.

"You're not frightened of me, are you?" Uncle Ned cried, dismay and unhappiness in his face.

"No!" cried Thomas, surprised to find that this was true. "No, no! Oh no! *No!*"

"But frightened of something, eh? Come on, then. Tell me. Tell me what. Two heads are better than one. We'll face it together."

"The dragon," Thomas said, almost wailing.

Uncle Ned said nothing for a moment. They stood staring at one another, he and Thomas, and Thomas saw one thought after another change the expression on his uncle's big face.

"Better come home," said Uncle Ned at last. "It's chilly out here, and you've got to be brave. I'll help you all I can."

He held out his hand and slowly, very slowly, Thomas put his own into it. Uncle Ned's hand was big and it was hard, as might be expected, but it was also very warm. It was a good thing to hang on to, Thomas decided.

A little short of home, Uncle Ned stopped and looked down at Thomas.

"I'll tell you what," he said. "If you'd rather, we needn't open the Dragon Box at all. It can stay tight closed for as long as you wish – for always, if need be. I'll give you the key to hide or throw away. All the same, it would be better to see if the dragon's as bad as you think. For to tell the truth, Thomas, they hardly ever are."

They went into the house together, and there was the box. No one was about, for Mamma and Florence were in the parlour, unrolling the Chinese carpet from its wrappings and crying out in excitement at the colour and the pattern.

"Well?" said Uncle Ned to Thomas.

"Open it," said Thomas.

"Take the key. Open it for yourself, if you really want to."

"Don't go away," said Thomas.

41

He took the key that Uncle Ned had unhooked from his watch-chain. His fingers fumbled at the keyhole, but at last the key slid home and nothing remained but for Thomas to turn it and fling open the lid.

"You can still change your mind," Uncle Ned told him.

Thomas glanced at him very quickly. Why had he ever minded that he was so big and booming? If he were not, then he would be someone different, and not Thomas's Uncle Ned at all. And that, there was no doubt of it, would be a pity..

As he thought that, Thomas quickly
flung up the lid of the Dragon Box.
Then he opened his eyes, that he had
squeezed shut. He saw that the box
was crammed with all manner of
things. But the dragon was on top.

"Take it," said Uncle Ned.

Thomas took the dragon out of the
box carefully and using both hands.
He looked at it slowly and for a long
minute – at its beautiful bright colours
and its fiery eyes, at its long twisting
tail with the green and silver scales, at
its wings, folded flat to its side just
now, but ready all the same to fly.

"A kite!" said Thomas at last. "A dragon kite," he said, his voice squeaking. "A dragon from the Land of the Dragon. It's mine. It's a dragon of my own – my very own dragon – isn't it, Uncle Ned?"

"Have you flown a kite before?"

"Not ever."

"Good. Then I can teach you. That'll be fun for me, too."

"Tomorrow?"

"If the wind's right."

"Morning," said Thomas firmly.

"Morning it is."

Thomas stood a second longer. He was beside himself with excitement, and with the beauty of the dragon which already in his imagination he saw sailing above the trees in the park. How the tail would lash, how the wings would spread – this was the most wonderful present he had ever been given. How dreadful it would be if he had no Uncle Ned to bring him such a gift from the far ends of the earth...

Suddenly his excitement burst out of him. He went stamping and shouting into the parlour, yelling out in a big boastful voice:

"I was right! I was right! There *was* a dragon in the Dragon Box!"

He saw Florence looking at him, the light glinting on her round, mended spectacles, so that he could not see her eyes.

"I told you!" cried Thomas.

Caerleon
Library